Lost in New York

JOHN ESCOTT

Level 2

Series Editors: Andy Hopkins and Jocelyn Potter

Pearson Education Limited

Edinburgh Gate, Harlow,
Essex CM20 2JE, England
and Associated Companies throughout the world.

ISBN: 978-1-4058-7697-1

First published by Penguin Books 2000
This edition first published by Pearson Education 2008

1 3 5 7 9 10 8 6 4 2

Copyright © Pearson Education Ltd 2008
Illustrations by Lyn Bruce

Typeset by Graphicraft Ltd, Hong Kong
Set in 11/14pt Bembo
Printed in China
SWTC/01

Published by Pearson Education Ltd in association with
Penguin Books Ltd, both companies being subsidiaries of Pearson Plc

Contents

Introduction

In the dream, he was always lost. Lost and afraid. He ran and ran. But, in the dream, hands always stopped him.

'But this isn't a dream,' he thought now. 'I'm lost in New York!'

This is Nicky's first visit to New York – the city of tall buildings and fast black and white police cars. He knows the place from TV, and now he is here. But he is afraid. He doesn't want to be here; he wants to be at home. It is his first visit to the United States, and his first visit to another country without his parents.

Nicky is going to stay with his aunt, but things quickly begin to go wrong. Where is his aunt? Who is Lou? And who are the boys on motorbikes? The boys take Nicky through the streets of New York. He doesn't want to go with them, but what can he do? And then he meets Melissa – a thief.

Not long after he arrives, the police are looking for Nicky. He has to find Aunt Carrie, or the strange Mrs Minerva. He has to find them before the police find him.

This is worse than any of Nicky's bad dreams!

John Escott enjoys reading and writing exciting stories. He writes books for students of all ages. When he is not writing, he likes walking by the sea. He also looks for old books in small bookshops. He lives in Bournemouth, a large town by the sea in the south of England.

His other books for Penguin Readers are *The Missing Coins*, *The Climb*, *Detective Work* and *The Ghost of Genny Castle*.

Chapter 1   New York

The aeroplane moved through the blue sky. Nicky looked out of the window.

'I'm not dreaming,' he thought. 'We *are* flying over New York!' Nicky felt afraid. 'I didn't want to come,' he thought. 'I wanted to stay at home.'

His parents could not come with him. His mother had to go into hospital. His father had to work.

'It's going to be OK,' he thought. 'Aunt Carrie is going to meet me at the airport. And it's going to be exciting.'

He turned away from the window and closed his eyes.

'It's my first visit to the USA,' Nicky thought. 'And it's my first time outside England without Mum and Dad.'

After a minute, he opened his eyes again. There was a woman next to him. She smiled at him.

'We'll be there in about ten minutes,' she said. 'Are you excited?'

'Er – yes,' said Nicky.

The United States of America . . .

Nicky thought of pictures in books. He thought of tall buildings and of fast black and white police cars in the streets.

And he thought of New York. Now he could see it below him.

'I'm going to stay with my Aunt Carrie,' he told the woman. 'She wrote me a letter. She has a restaurant in Manhattan.'

'. . . Come and stay with me when your mother goes into hospital,' she wrote in her letter. 'I can show you all the interesting places in New York.'

'We're going down to JFK, the airport, now,' the woman told Nicky.

And she was right. The aeroplane went down . . . down . . . The buildings below got bigger and bigger. And then the plane was on the ground.

He was in New York!

'I hope Aunt Carrie's at the airport,' Nicky thought.

There was somebody there. But it wasn't Aunt Carrie.

Chapter 2   Boys on Motorbikes

A man met Nicky at the airport.

'Who are you?' Nicky asked him.

'I'm Lou,' said the man. He smiled. 'I work at the restaurant with your aunt.'

The man was very fat. His stomach came out over the top of his trousers. His green shirt was too small for him.

'Where's Aunt Carrie?' Nicky asked. He didn't like strangers. He was afraid of them.

'She had an accident this morning,' Lou said. 'She fell on a wet floor in the kitchen, and she hurt her leg. She's OK, but she couldn't come to the airport. "I'll meet Nicky," I told her.'

He took Nicky's bag. Then he put a hand on the boy's arm. His hand was big and fat and strong.

'Let's get a taxi,' he said. 'I have to stop at Sam's Meat Shop on the way back, but only for five minutes.'

Nicky followed him to the taxi. Lou was big and fat but he moved quickly. The taxi driver put Nicky's bag in the back of the car. Nicky and Lou got into the taxi, and they drove away from the airport with a lot of other cars and buses.

It was a beautiful, sunny morning. They went across a bridge, but Nicky couldn't see the river below it.

Aunt Carrie lived in Manhattan. Manhattan is in New York. It is a long, thin island with a lot of tall buildings. Nicky could see some of the buildings through the taxi windows.

They drove off the bridge on to the island. Nicky looked up . . . and up . . . and up. The buildings were really very tall, but after some time, they got smaller.

'Mrs Minerva couldn't meet you today,' Lou told Nicky. He smiled.

'Mum didn't tell me about Mrs Minerva or Lou,' Nicky thought. 'Does she know them? And does Mrs Minerva work at the restaurant too?'

'It's Friday today,' Lou said. 'Friday is Mrs Minerva's boat day. You'll like Mrs Minerva.'

'Has Mrs Minerva got a boat?' Nicky said.

Lou laughed. 'No,' he said. 'It's one of the tour boats. It goes round Manhattan. Mrs Minerva likes to go on the two o'clock boat every Friday.'

The taxi turned into a small street and stopped outside a big shop. It sold meat.

'I have to get some things for the restaurant,' Lou said. 'I'll only be five minutes. Then we can walk to the restaurant.'

Lou took Nicky's bag and paid the taxi driver. The taxi drove away.

Nicky followed Lou to the shop and they went inside. There was a man in the shop. He looked up and saw Nicky and Lou. Then he smiled.

'How are you, Lou?' the man said.

'*I'm* OK,' Lou said, smiling. 'But Mrs Brady isn't happy with *you*, Sam.'

'Not happy?' said Sam. 'Why?'

'Last week's meat was bad,' Lou said. 'We couldn't use it. Mrs Brady had to throw it away. She was very angry.'

'But I don't understand,' Sam said. 'It was good meat—'

'Ha!' Lou laughed. 'Good? Mrs Brady didn't call it that! I want to see today's meat.'

'Of course! Of course!' Sam said. 'Come out to the back, Lou. Come and see it. We only send the best meat to Mrs Brady.'

Lou went with Sam. 'Wait there, Nicky,' he said. 'I won't be long.'

Lou and Sam went through a door at the back of the shop. Then Nicky was alone. The sun came in through a window. The room got hotter and hotter. Nicky got hotter and hotter. He began to feel ill.

'I've got to go outside,' he thought. 'I can wait for Lou there.' He went out into the street.

Three boys were at the other end of the street. They were older than Nicky. They kicked a ball and shouted. There were two motorbikes near them. One was yellow. The other was black and had an open sidecar.

Nicky watched the young men. Then an old woman came out of a building.

'Go away!' she shouted at them.

They laughed at her. Then one boy got on the motorbike with the sidecar. The other two climbed on to the yellow bike.

The motorbikes came up the street. The three boys laughed and shouted.

Then they saw Nicky. The two boys on the yellow motorbike began to ride round and round the street. They watched Nicky and said something. Then they laughed.

The third young man stopped his motorbike and sidecar near Nicky. 'Hi,' he said. He had red hair. He was about three years older than Nicky.

'Hello,' Nicky said.

'Hello,' said 'Red Hair'. He tried to sound as English as Nicky. Then the three young men laughed.

'Are you English?' said Red Hair.

'Yes,' Nicky said. 'Where's Lou?' he thought. 'I don't like these people.'

'Hey, Jake! Pete! He's English,' shouted Red Hair to the other two young men. They rode across the street on the yellow motorbike and stopped behind Red Hair. The boy on the back of the yellow motorbike got off. He walked across to Nicky.

'What's your name?' he asked.

'Nicky,' Nicky told him.

'Nice shirt,' he said. He smiled.

Nicky didn't like that smile. It wasn't a nice smile. The other young men smiled too.

'Come here,' Red Hair said to Nicky.

Nicky didn't move.

'Do it,' Jake said. And he pushed Nicky.

Nicky stopped next to the open sidecar. He looked back at the shop door. 'Where's Lou?' he thought.

'What are you doing here?' Red Hair asked him.

'I – I'm waiting,' Nicky said.

'That's boring,' Jake said. 'Do you want to come with us? *We're* not boring.'

And he pushed Nicky again.

Nicky fell and something hit the back of his legs. It was the sidecar. Suddenly, Nicky was in the sidecar! Red Hair started the bike.

'Stop!' Nicky shouted.

'Go!' shouted Jake.

And the motorbike and sidecar rode away fast.

Chapter 3   Girl Thief!

'Stop!' Nicky shouted again.

But Red Hair didn't stop. He laughed.

Jake and Pete followed on the yellow motorbike, and they laughed too.

Red Hair went through more and more streets. They were a long way from Sam's shop now. The buildings round them were high. There were more cars and buses on the roads. Nicky saw a police car, but it was too fast. He couldn't stop it.

'I'll never find the shop again!' Nicky thought. 'I'll never find Lou or Aunt Carrie or Mrs Minerva. Where are these young men taking me?'

Suddenly, Red Hair stopped the motorbike. Nicky sat up in the sidecar. He planned to get out. But then the yellow motorbike stopped next to him.

Jake smiled at Nicky. 'Are you all right, boy?' he said.

'I've got to get back!' Nicky said. 'Take me back!'

Red Hair laughed. 'Pete will take you back later,' he said.

'You can go in ten minutes,' Pete told him. 'It's OK, Nicky.'

Jake got off the back of the yellow motorbike. They were outside a building with a green front door. A woman sat outside the door and smoked a cigarette. She had brown hair and wore a red skirt with green flowers on it. She watched Nicky and the other boys but said nothing.

A minute later, a girl came out of the building. She was about sixteen years old. She wore jeans and a blue shirt. She had brown hair, too.

'I'm going out, Mum,' the girl said to the woman. 'See you later.'

The girl's mother looked at her, then at the boys. 'Don't do anything bad,' she told the girl. But the girl laughed.

'Hi, Melissa!' shouted Jake.

The girl ran across to the motorbikes. She looked at Nicky, then turned to the other young men. 'Who's this?' she said.

'His name's Nicky,' Red Hair said. 'He's English.'

'Where did he come from?' she asked.

The young men laughed. 'We . . . found him,' Jake said. 'He wanted a ride.'

'Let's go,' Red Hair said. He looked at the girl's mother. 'Are you ready, Melissa?'

The girl got on the motorbike behind him. Jake got on the other motorbike again.

The girl looked down at Nicky from the back of the motorbike. She smiled.

'Are you a visitor to New York?' she asked.

'Yes,' said Nicky.

'Take him on a tour, Red,' she said to the young man in front of her.

Red Hair smiled. 'OK,' he said.

Nicky didn't want a tour of New York. He wanted to get back to Lou. But suddenly they rode fast through the streets again. They went past cars and buses. Now and then, Melissa shouted to Nicky.

'This is Times Square . . .

'This is Broadway. . .

'Now we're on Fifth Avenue.'

Then the motorbikes stopped. Nicky looked round. Were they near Sam's shop?

No, they weren't.

Melissa looked at a big shop. 'That shop sells everything,' she told Nicky. 'Do you want to go shopping?'

'No,' Nicky said. 'I want to go back–'

'Later,' Red Hair said. 'Melissa's going shopping now. You can go with her.' He pulled Nicky out of the sidecar and pushed him across to the shop doors. Melissa went inside, and Nicky followed her. Jake, Pete and Red Hair waited with their motorbikes.

Nicky wanted to run away. But where to? He didn't know New York. He couldn't find Sam's shop or Aunt Carrie's restaurant.

'I've got to stay with these people,' he thought. 'They've got to take me back.'

There were a lot of people in the shop. Melissa moved quickly. She stopped now and then and looked at something – a skirt or some jeans, a scarf or a hat. She put a hat on her head and laughed. A woman watched her.

'Do you want to buy it?' she asked Melissa.

'No thanks,' laughed Melissa. And she gave the hat to the woman. The woman turned and put the hat behind her.

Suddenly, Nicky could feel somebody's hand. It pushed something inside his shirt. He wanted to say something, but Melissa kicked him.

'Shh!' she said. Then she walked quickly away.

After a minute or two, they were near some clocks and watches. Melissa began to look at the clocks. A man came across.

'Can I help you?' he asked her.

'How much is this clock?' asked Melissa.

'Fifty-two dollars,' the man said.

'That's too expensive,' said Melissa. 'Have you got anything cheaper?'

'Yes,' the man said. He turned away from them.

Melissa's hand moved quickly. She took a watch and pushed it inside her shirt.

Nicky wanted to run. He wanted to get away from this girl, this *thief*! Then the man turned round again. There was a different clock in his hand.

'This clock is only eighteen dollars,' he told Melissa.

She took it and looked at it. Then she gave it back to him. 'Sorry, it's too expensive,' she said.

'That's our cheapest clock,' said the man.

'That's OK,' Melissa said.

She put her hand on Nicky's arm and they moved away. Melissa looked round, but nobody followed them. She did this four times before she went outside.

'Let's go,' she told Nicky. She began to run down the street.

Nicky ran behind her. He put his hand into his shirt and pulled out an expensive scarf.

'Thanks,' Melissa said. She took the scarf from him.

Red Hair, Jake and Pete were in the next street.

'What did you get?' Pete asked Melissa.

She showed them the watch and the scarf. 'We can get some more things later,' she said. 'Let's get away from here.'

'Take me back,' Nicky said. 'Or tell me the address of Sam's shop. I can get a taxi.'

'Be quiet!' Jake said. 'We'll take you back later.'

Chapter 4   A Bad Dream

The motorbikes moved between cars and buses again. Melissa was on the back of Red Hair's motorbike. She laughed and shouted to him. Jake and Pete were behind them. They knew the streets and avenues of the city. Nicky sat in the sidecar. He began to feel ill.

'When will they take me back to Lou?' he thought. 'Will he be there?'

Red Hair turned off from the wide avenue of tall buildings and stopped in a small street.

'This isn't the right street,' Nicky said. 'Where's Sam's shop?'

'Be quiet,' Red Hair told him. He got off the motorbike. 'I'm feeling hungry.'

Nicky got out of the sidecar. 'Tell me the name of the right street,' he said. He pulled Red Hair's arm. 'I can get a taxi from here.'

Red Hair pushed him away. 'Be quiet!' he said again. He was angry now.

Jake got off the other motorbike and walked across to them. They were near a shop. There was fruit outside it.

Jake and Red Hair walked across to the shop. Jake looked at the fruit and smiled. 'Peaches,' he said. 'I'd like a peach.'

He took one and began to eat it. Then he took three more peaches and threw them to Red Hair, Pete and Melissa.

'Do you want one?' he said to Nicky.

'No,' Nicky said.

Jake laughed. 'Yes, you do!' He took another peach and threw it to Nicky. 'Catch!' he said, and laughed.

Nicky caught the peach.

'Hey, you!' somebody shouted at Nicky.

It was the fruit-seller. He ran out of his shop.

'Run!' Jake shouted to Nicky.

Nicky couldn't move. 'It's a bad dream,' he thought. 'I want to wake up, but I can't.'

Other people looked at him now. A car came up the street.

It was a police car.

Nicky couldn't move.

'Police!' Melissa shouted.

Jake and Red Hair ran and jumped on their motorbikes. They all laughed and shouted. Then they rode away.

Nicky felt a hand on his arm. The hand was big and strong. It was the man from the shop, and he was angry.

'I've got you!' he said to Nicky.

'I – I didn't do anything!' Nicky said.

'He's English,' somebody said.

'He's a thief,' said the man from the shop.

The police car stopped suddenly. Two policemen got out. They started to walk across the street to Nicky.

Nicky was afraid. 'The police think I'm a thief!' he thought. 'What's Aunt Carrie going to say?'

The two policemen were nearer now.

'I don't want to talk to these policemen,' he thought. 'I'm not a thief. But they think I am!'

Suddenly, Nicky pulled away from the fruit-seller and ran.

They shouted. The policemen started to run. Other people shouted. They all tried to stop Nicky, but Nicky was a fast runner.

He didn't look back – he ran!

'They won't catch me,' he thought. 'But now I'm lost!'

Chapter 5   Alone in New York

The sun was hot on Nicky's head. He looked up at the tall buildings. He felt very small and afraid. The noise of cars and buses hurt his head. He stopped running and started to walk. He pushed through people. There was nobody – no police officers – behind him now.

'Where am I?' he thought. 'What am I going to do? How can I find Aunt Carrie's restaurant? This is my worst dream!'

He often had that dream. In the dream, he was always lost. Lost and afraid. He ran and ran. But, in the dream, hands always stopped him.

'But this isn't a dream,' he thought now. 'I'm lost in New York!'

He didn't know the name of Aunt Carrie's street. Her address was in his bag, and his bag was in Sam's shop.

He was outside an office window now. It was a bus tour office. There were words on the inside of the window. Nicky stopped and read them.

Go on a tour of Chinatown. Take a tour of Harlem. See Greenwich Village. Bus and boat tours round New York. Come inside!

A boat! Nicky remembered Lou's words: '... Mrs Minerva likes to go on the two o'clock boat...' The boat tour round Manhattan.

'Perhaps I can find the tour boat!' he thought. 'Then perhaps I can find Mrs Minerva.'

There was a clock in the office window. Nicky looked at the time. It was one o'clock.

'I only have an hour,' he thought. 'Can I find the tour boat in an hour?'

He went into the office. There was a woman at a desk. She looked up when Nicky came in. 'Yes?' she said. 'Can I help you?'

'I want to catch the two o'clock boat tour,' he said. 'Can I get a bus to the boat?'

'No,' the woman said. 'That bus went at half past twelve. It goes on a tour of Greenwich Village first.'

'When's the next bus?' Nicky asked.

'Not before two o'clock,' the woman told him.

'Where does the boat go from?' Nicky asked.

'Pier 83,' the woman said.

She looked away from Nicky and began to talk into a telephone. Two more people pushed past him. They wanted to speak to the woman.

Nicky came out of the bus tour office.

'I've got to find Pier 83,' he thought. 'I've got to get on that boat. But how will I know Mrs Minerva?'

Chapter 6   A Taxi Ride

A bus stood outside the tour office. The driver read a newspaper.

'Excuse me,' Nicky said.

The driver looked at him. 'Yes?' he said.

'Where's Pier 83, please?' Nicky asked.

'It's at the end of West 43rd Street,' the driver said.

'Everything has a number in New York,' Nicky said. 'Streets, avenues, piers.'

'Are you English?' the driver said.

'Yes,' Nicky said.

'Why are you alone?' the driver said.

'I—' began Nicky.

'Are you lost?' the driver said. 'There's a policeman over there. Perhaps he can help you.'

Nicky looked across the street – and saw a policeman.

'It's all right,' Nicky said quickly. 'I'm not lost.'

He didn't want to talk to any policemen. Policemen asked questions and Nicky didn't want to answer any questions.

He went the other way. He looked at the names of roads and avenues. Numbers, all numbers. He walked down small streets. After some time, the buildings got smaller and darker. Some of their windows had wood over them. Nicky didn't like these streets. He felt afraid.

He walked into the road. A car driver shouted at him, and Nicky moved back quickly. He turned – and walked into a man. The man was a taxi driver.

'Hey!' he said.

'Sorry,' Nicky said.

'Where are you going?' the taxi driver asked. 'You're not from round here.'

'Pier 83,' Nicky said. 'I'm looking for Pier 83.'

'You're in the wrong place,' the taxi driver said. 'It's a long way from here.'

'But I've got to be at Pier 83 before two o'clock,' Nicky said.

'Have you?' said the taxi driver. 'Why?'

'I've got to go on a boat and find Mrs Minerva,' said Nicky. 'And–'

'Stop!' The taxi driver looked at Nicky. 'Are you English?' he asked.

'Yes,' Nicky said.

'And you're lost, right?' the man said. 'OK, I'll take you to Pier 83.'

'But I can't pay you. I've only got four or five dollars,' Nicky said. 'I'll want those for the boat tour. My other money is in my bag and–'

'It's OK,' the driver told him. 'Forget about the money. I'll take you.' He smiled. 'A nice ride for my young friend from England.'

Nicky smiled back. 'Thanks,' he said.

'Let's go,' said the taxi driver. 'We haven't got much time.'

Nicky got into the taxi. He sat down and felt better. He was tired, and his feet hurt. They drove down the street and into a wide avenue. The driver drove in and out of the cars and buses. Sometimes he shouted at a driver in a different taxi. But it wasn't an angry shout. For the first time that day, Nicky stopped feeling afraid.

'Why are you alone?' the taxi driver asked him. 'How did you get lost?'

'I was . . . it was a mistake,' Nicky said. He didn't want to tell the driver about Melissa or Red Hair, or the other boys. He didn't want to tell him about the peach or the policemen.

'A mistake?' said the man. 'What do you mean?'

'I lost the person with me,' Nicky said. 'Now I'm looking for somebody on the boat. Her name is Mrs Minerva. She always goes on the two o'clock boat tour round Manhattan on Fridays.'

'And you're hoping to find her?' the taxi driver asked.

'Yes,' Nicky said.

'Do you know her face?' the driver said.

'No,' Nicky said.

'Then how will you find her? It will be difficult,' the man said.

They turned into other streets, other wide avenues. Were they too late for the boat? But then, between two buildings at the end of the street, Nicky saw the water with the sun on it. And there was the pier. Pier 83.

A boat was next to the pier, and people were on it. Some of them had cameras. Some were Americans, and some were from other countries.

'Is that the tour boat?' Nicky asked.

'Yes,' the taxi driver said. 'I hope you find your Mrs Minerva.'

'Thanks,' Nicky said. He got out of the taxi. 'Thanks for the ride.'

Chapter 7   The Girl on the Boat

A small girl was on the boat. Her name was Sarah Washington. She sat next to her mother and looked at the water.

'You'll see the George Washington Bridge,' her mother said.

'*Our* name is Washington,' said the girl.

Her mother smiled. 'I know,' she said. 'But Washington is also the name of a famous American President. Our boat is going to go under the bridge.'

They were on the top deck of the boat. There was a guard-rail round the deck. Sarah sat next to the guard-rail and looked across to the stairs. The stairs came up from the deck below.

'Can we eat something?' Sarah asked. 'They're selling food on the deck below.'

'Later,' said her mother.

A boy came up the stairs. He looked round for somebody.

'We're moving now,' Sarah's mother said.

The boat moved away from Pier 83.

Nicky didn't have any money now.

'I hope I find Mrs Minerva,' he thought. 'I've got no money for a taxi. And I've got no money for a hotel.'

He wanted to close his eyes. He wanted to wake up from this bad dream. But it wasn't a dream.

The boat moved through the water, past the buildings of Manhattan. It was warm and there was no wind. There were a lot of people on the top deck of the boat.

'A lot of faces,' Nicky thought. 'Thin faces, fat faces, old faces. Which is Mrs Minerva?'

A man walked past Nicky. He had books about the boat tour. People gave him money and took the books from him. He looked back at Nicky and then moved down the deck.

'How old is Mrs Minerva?' Nicky thought. 'Is she as old as Aunt Carrie?'

Then they went past the most famous statue in the world. The Statue of Liberty.

The statue was on an island, and the boat went round it. People moved across the boat, and looked at it. A woman walked into Nicky.

'Excuse me,' she said.

'Are – are you Mrs Minerva?' Nicky asked her.

The woman took some photos. 'No,' she said. 'Why?'

'I've got to find her,' Nicky said. He moved away.

He sat down and tried to think.

'Do I have to ask every woman, "Are you Mrs Minerva?"?' he thought. 'How much time have I got on this boat? Two hours? Three?'

He saw a small girl. She wasn't interested in the Statue of Liberty. She moved away from the other people and stood next to the guard-rail. She had an ice-cream on a stick. After a minute or two, she finished the ice-cream. Then she put her hand over the guard-rail and the stick fell into the water. Next, the girl climbed up on to the guard-rail and looked down. She watched the stick. It moved away in the water.

Nicky stood up.

'Why's she up there?' he thought. 'That's stupid. She'll fall into the water!'

The girl looked down at the stick. Her mother was across the boat. Her eyes were on the Statue of Liberty.

'Her mother doesn't know,' thought Nicky. 'Her daughter is on the guard-rail, and she doesn't know!'

Nicky forgot about Mrs Minerva and his problems. He thought only about the small girl.

Suddenly, her mother turned and saw her.

'Sarah!' she shouted. 'Sarah, no!'

The small girl turned round quickly – and began to fall back over the guard-rail! Her mother started to run across the deck to her. Other people saw the girl and began to run, too.

'They won't catch her,' Nicky thought. 'She'll fall into the water!'

He ran.

Sarah cried out. 'Aaagh, I'm falling!'

Two hands stopped her.

They were Nicky's hands.

Chapter 8   Mrs Minerva!

'Oh, thank you, thank you!' Sarah's mother said to Nicky. She had her arms round her daughter. The little girl cried loudly.

'It's all right,' Nicky said.

There were a lot of people round him now.

'You can move quickly,' a man said.

'You're a fast runner,' a woman told him.

'Are you alone?' somebody asked him. It was the man with the tour books.

'Yes,' Nicky said. 'But I'm looking for somebody.'

'Who?' asked the man.

'Her name's Mrs Minerva,' said Nicky,

'Mrs Minerva?' the man said. He laughed.

'Do you know her?' asked Nicky.

'Yes, I know Mrs Minerva!' said the man. 'She comes on this boat every week. Lou brings her every Friday.'

'Do you know Lou?' Nicky said.

'Yes, I know Lou,' said the man. 'He works at Carrie Brady's restaurant. He's my friend. My name's Joe.'

'Is Mrs Minerva here now?' Nicky asked.

'Oh yes, she's here,' said Joe, smiling,

'I've got to talk to her,' said Nicky. 'I want her to take me to Aunt Carrie's restaurant.'

'Come with me,' Joe said. He laughed. 'Come and talk to Mrs Minerva.'

He took Nicky down the stairs to the deck below. Some people were at the bar. They bought drinks and sandwiches. Other people looked out across the water at the island of Manhattan.

'Mrs Minerva is at the front of the boat,' he told Nicky. 'She likes to sit at the front.'

Nicky followed him to the front of the boat. 'I hope Mrs

Minerva is nice,' he thought. 'I hope she's not angry with me.'

'Meet Mrs Minerva!' Joe said, and he laughed again.

Nicky looked – *and saw a monkey!*

'That – that's Mrs Minerva?' Nicky said. His eyes opened wide. 'A monkey?'

The monkey was on the guard-rail. It watched Nicky with its small eyes.

'Yes,' Joe said. 'She's Lou's monkey. I bring her on the boat every Friday because Lou has to work late.' He smiled. 'Mrs Minerva likes a boat ride!'

Nicky sat down next to Mrs Minerva and started to laugh. The monkey jumped into his arms.

'Now you can enjoy the boat tour,' Joe told him. 'I'll phone the restaurant after we get back. Lou can come and get you.'

'What are you going to tell him?' asked Nicky.

'I'll say, "Nicky caught a little girl before she fell into the water! Everybody thinks he's great!" ' said Joe.

Nicky smiled. 'I'm only here because I got lost in New York. It was a bad dream!'

'But your bad dream is ending happily,' Joe said.

And he was right.

ACTIVITIES

Chapters 1–2

Before you read

1 Look at the Word List at the back of the book. What are the words in your language?
2 Read the Introduction to the book. Then answer these questions.
   a Where is Nicky going?
   b Who is going with him?
   c Who is he going to stay with?
3 Is Nicky going to enjoy his visit? Why (not)? What do you think?

While you read

4 Write short answers to these questions.
   a Where is Nicky? ....
   b Where is his mother? ....
   c Where in New York is his aunt's restaurant? ....
   d Who meets him at the airport? ....
   e Who goes on tour boats on Fridays? ....
   f Who sells meat to Nicky's aunt? ....
   g Who has a motorbike with a sidecar? ....
   h Who pushes Nicky into the sidecar? ....

After you read

5 Who says or thinks these words?
   a 'I didn't want to come.'
   b 'Mrs Minerva couldn't meet you today.'
   c 'We only send the best meat to Mrs Brady.'
   d 'I've got to go outside.'
   e 'Are you English?'
   f 'Do you want to come with us? *We're* not boring.'
6 Work with another student. Have this conversation.
   Student A: You are Jake. You see Nicky down the street. You want to play a game with him. What do you say to Pete?
   Student B: You are Pete. Answer Jake. What are the two of you going to do with Nicky? Talk about it.

Chapters 3–4

Before you read

7 Look at the pictures on pages 9 and 12, and discuss these questions.

    a Who and what can you see?

    b What is happening?

    c What is going to happen next?

While you read

8 Are these sentences right (✓) or wrong (✗)?

    a Red Hair takes Nicky a long way.   .....

    b Melissa has a motorbike too.   .....

    c Melissa buys a clock.   .....

    d Melissa takes a watch from the shop.   .....

    e Melissa puts a scarf inside Nicky's shirt.   .....

    f Nicky is enjoying the ride.   .....

    g Red Hair buys a peach.   .....

    h The fruit-seller runs after Nicky.   .....

    i Nicky runs away.   .....

    j He is lost in New York.   .....

After you read

9 Finish these sentences.

    a Melissa lives …

    b Melissa takes Nicky …

    c There, she takes …

    d Jake and Red Hair go …

    e Jake takes …

    f The older boys and Melissa …

    g The policemen think …

10 Work with another student. Have this conversation.

    Student A: You are the man in the shop. You can't find the watch, but you remember the girl. Tell your boss.

    Student B: You are the man's boss, and you are angry. Ask questions. What do you want the man to do now? Tell him.

Chapters 5–6

Before you read

11 In these chapters, do you think that:
- **a** the police will catch Nicky?
- **b** Nicky will find Sam's shop?
- **c** Nicky will find Aunt Carrie's restaurant?
- **d** Nicky will find Mrs Minerva?

While you read

12 Write a word in each sentence.
- **a** The .... of the cars and buses hurts Nicky's head.
- **b** He doesn't know the name of Aunt Carrie's street. He hasn't got her ....
- **c** He reads in an office window about bus and boat ....
- **d** The boat leaves from .... 83.
- **e** Nicky talks to a bus driver, but he doesn't want to talk to any ....
- **f** A .... driver takes him to the river.

After you read

13 When and why does Nicky stop feeling afraid?

14 Work with another student. Have a conversation.
- *Student A*: You are the taxi driver. Tell your wife about the lost boy.
- *Student B*: You are the taxi driver's wife. Ask questions.

Chapters 7–8

Before you read

15 What will Nicky do on the boat? How will he find Mrs Minerva? Discuss these questions.

While you read

16 Use one of these words in each question: *How, What, Which, Where, Who, Why*. Then write the number of each answer.

a .... bridge has the name of a famous American
President?   .....

b .... are there a lot of people on the boat?   .....

c .... stops a girl falling into the water?   .....

d .... on the boat is Mrs Minerva?   .....

e .... is Mrs Minerva?   .....

f .... does Nicky's bad dream end?   .....

1) Because it is a boat tour.   **4)** A monkey.

2) At the front.   **5)** George Washington Bridge.

3) Happily.   **6)** Nicky.

After you read

17 Discuss the picture on pages 20–21. What can you see in the picture? Who can you see? What are they doing? What happened before this? What is going to happen?

Writing

18 You are Lou. You arrive at the restaurant without Nicky. Write your conversation with Aunt Carrie.

19 You are Sarah's mother. Write a letter to a friend. Tell her about Sarah and the boy on the boat.

20 You are Nicky. It is a week after the story ends. Write a postcard to your parents. Don't tell them about your first day!

21 Write about Melissa, Jake and Red Hair. Why do they take things?

22 Were you lost in a town or city? What happened? How did you feel? Write about it.

23 Do you have bad dreams? Write about one of them.

WORD LIST *with example sentences*

alone (adj) After everybody left, I was *alone* in the house.

avenue (n) You turn off the wide *avenue* onto his street.

deck (n) When the boat left, everybody was on the *deck*.

dream (n/v) He wakes up every night because he has very bad *dreams*.

guard-rail (n) The *guard-rail* stops people falling into the river.

island (n) You can take a boat from here to the *islands*.

lost (adj) We were *lost* in Tokyo and we didn't speak Japanese.

monkey (n) *Monkeys* jumped from tree to tree.

motorbike (n) Be careful on that *motorbike*! Please don't go fast.

peach (n) We like all fruit, but in the summer we buy a lot of *peaches*.

pier (n) He stood on the *pier* and watched the boats.

president (n) Roosevelt was the *President* of the United States four times.

ride (n/v) Can I go for a *ride* on your horse?

scarf (n) It is very cold outside, Are you going to wear a hat and a *scarf*?

sidecar (n) I am a driver, so I don't like sitting in a *sidecar*.

statue (n) There are *statues* of famous people in every park.

stick (n) He hits his children with a *stick*!

sunny (adj) It's a *sunny* day! Let's go outside.

thief (n) A *thief* in her office took the money from her bag.

tour (n) We are going on a bus *tour* of India next month.